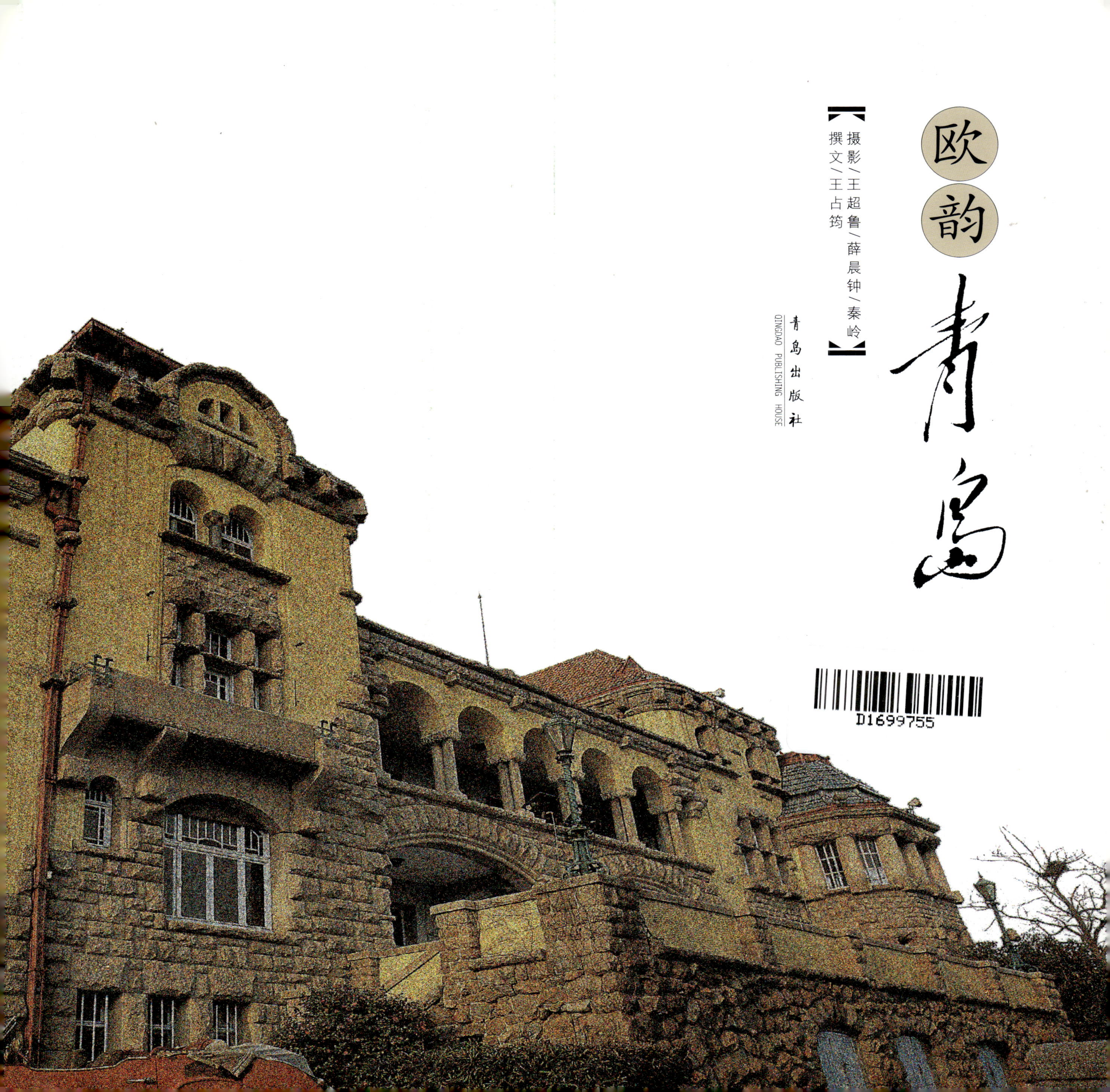
欧韵
青岛
摄影／王超鲁／薛晨钟／秦岭
撰文／王占筠
青岛出版社
QINGDAO PUBLISHING HOUSE
D1699755

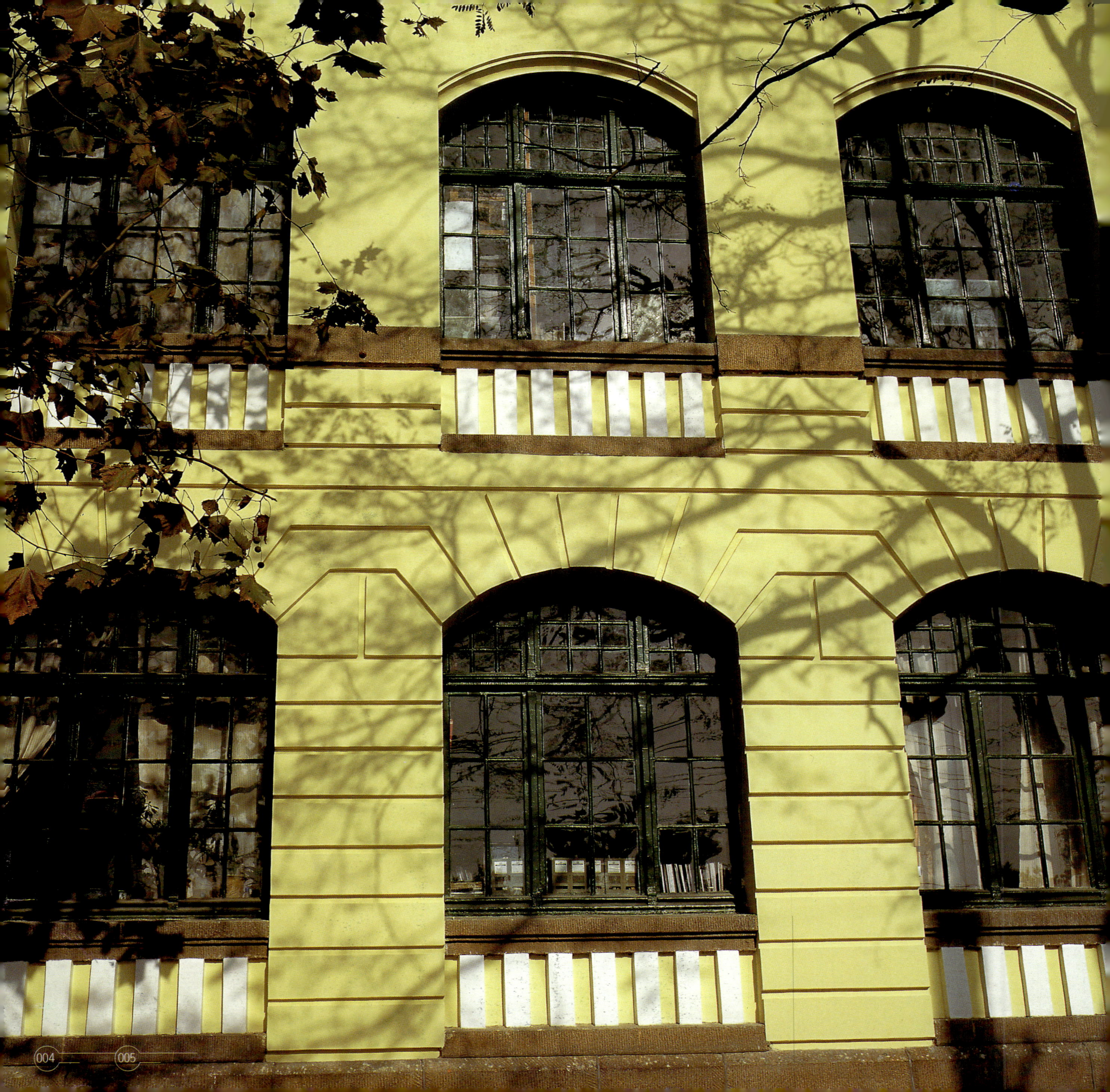

叙

Preface

一个全新的城市缺少回味，一个兀自老去的城市没有惊喜，只有新旧交汇的城市，才是一杯妖娆的鸡尾酒。

青岛天天上演双城记，欧韵的老城那些往日的风华，至今仍萦绕在回廊的拐角，牵挂在后花园的老石榴树上，暗藏在雀巢一样的阁楼里。历练百年而不衰，留给城市一个沉稳而倔强的剪影。新城区的变化却在分秒之间，她像出身贵族的小姐，未成年，尚不会矜持，只一味地张扬着自身的美好，留给城市一个浪漫的倩影。

除了沉稳倔强和浪漫，青岛最大的特质就是欧陆风范——这也是青岛以"洋气"闻名于世的根本所在。溯源20世纪初德占时的青岛，提倡中世纪欧洲城市自由活泼、景色如画的规划手法，于是，德意志民族的古典复兴、浪漫主义和折衷主义，在这个海边的小镇身上构成了微观的欧洲近代城市风貌。20世纪30年代前期，由于青岛地区远离战火，政局比较安定，民族工商业获得较大发展，人口迅速膨胀，外国投资大量增加，下台的军阀和官僚也都看中这块相对安全的地域，纷纷向青岛迁移和投资——这些背景使得青岛的城市建设又出现一次高潮。留学归来的中国设计师纷纷在这凭海临风的佳地上实践着灵感，一批批现代风格的国际式住宅又为城市增添了亮丽的色彩。

一座欧韵的城市就这样成长起来。红瓦高低错落，街巷起伏蜿蜒，教堂钟声回荡于街角城区，塔楼的尖顶掩映于山坡绿丛。

百年城市，百年海港。东西方文化潮涨潮落、水乳交融，浸润着青岛人的生活，青岛人原本开放、豪爽、追求时髦的性格也由此更加张扬。

青岛人生在海边，青岛人见过世面，青岛注定走向世界。

A brand new city has little historical attraction, whereas a self-closed old city has little surprise to offer. Only when a city comprises both the old and the new can it be enjoyed like a glass of romantically enchanting cocktail.

Such enchantment prevails in Qingdao. In the old city zone, one can find European-styled buildings like porch, backyard with old pomegranate trees, and nest-like attics. They have survived hundreds of years and are silhouetted strong against the city. However, the new city zone changes every second. It looks like a young lady from a noble family who does not know how to be reserved but showing off her youthfulness and beauty. All the changes bring the city lots of romance and beauty.

Apart from its old charm and new romance, Qingdao is famous for its "oreign flavor" because of its special European characteristics. Back in the early 20th century in German-occupied Qingdao, the city planning of a free, vigorous and picture-like European style of the Middle Ages was promoted. So the German's Classicism, Renaissance, Romanticism and Eclecticism have shaped this little coastal town into a miniature of modern European urban style. In early 1930s, since it was far away from the battles and had a peaceful environment, the national industry and commerce developed prosperously and its population grew quickly. Foreign investments increased a lot. Non-office-holding warlords and bureaucracies all settled on this peaceful land and invested in business. All these brought about another peak of the city's development. The returning overseas Chinese designers carried out their inspirational designs on this beautiful land and rows of buildings in modern international styles have added pretty colors to the city's landscape.

In such a way a European style city has developed. Red-roof buildings strew at random; winding streets and roads stretch far; toll of church bells echoes over streets; tower tops hide in the greens.

In this century-old port city, eastern and western cultures interact in complete harmony, nurturing Qingdao citizens. Their born openness, frankness and fashion-pursuit are therefore further expressed.

Qingdao people live by the sea, have rich experiences, and will surely walk up to the world.

城与海

暮色中的前海栈桥　The Pier at dusk

海与这个城市抱得异常紧。咸的氤氲中，生活川流不息。

海岸扛着日常的开支，几进几出；城市的性格、气质和情绪沿着海岸铺展开来，向东向西，自然结合人文，沧海桑田以后，海岸更加多情。

从城市诞生的那一天开始，就命中注定和海洋、港口、海外贸易密不可分，城市居民都保持着海港独有的开放传统，在过去一百年的岁月中，这座城市的名字被来自海外的船长、水手、商人、观光客用不同的语言热烈赞赏，这里输出的商品在世界各地流传。

外地人到青岛，不在看海，就在去看海的路上。比如，一个内陆城市的女小资，坐了三十多个小时的火车，带着与大海有关的主观臆想一路铿锵而来。甫出火车站，她不顾劳顿，循着潮声直驱第六海水浴场，行使她有生以来与大海的第一次接触。接下来，她在

CITY & Sea

The city of Qingdao, embraced by the sea, is bustling and brimming with life. It stretches along the coast, displaying its charms and passions.

Ever since its establishment, the city of Qingdao has been bonded with the ocean, the port and foreign trade. As a result the local people have always been open to new concepts and fashions. Over the past 100 years, the city has attracted sailors and merchants from different countries. Goods have been shipped from this port to all the corners of the world.

Most of the Chinese tourists have come to Qingdao to fulfill a long cherished dream: to see the ocean for the first time, to indulge themselves in the blue water or on the sands in the sunshine.

① 远眺太平路
A distant view of Taiping Road

② 八大关一瞥
A glimpse of Badaguan

① 俯瞰青岛湾　Qingdao Bay

青岛呆了七天，回到自己的城市后，把这段难忘的情绪写成感性文字贴在了社区里："我以为浪花都是为我而独特绽放的，我的意志被挑拨了，情感被晕染了，我躺在沙滩上，把自己摆成'大'字，思绪伸张为纷披的触须，刚好，阳光狠狠地透耀着我，充满着我，直到将灵魂净化了，并如晶体般澄澈。"

海让城市有了岸。很多时候，岸是用来眺望的，如果这种眺望没有遮挡，视线便可以幸运地飞远。早晨，当太阳的上缘与水面相切，红光骤然消逝，迸出的绿色的光霭让船体处于昏暗之中，而那些浅色的帆已被染成了紫红色。这样的美景常常很短促，用不了多久，海面上泛起的金光就平铺直叙了，世界忽然没了遮掩。

① 迎宾馆(原德占时期的总督官邸)
The Guest House, originally built by a German Governor

One woman was so impressed by Qingdao that she wrote:"I came to think every wave bore clusters of white blossoms just to give a feast to my eyes. Stretching my body on the sands, a multitude of feelers grew out of my mind. I could feel sunshine got through my skin into my soul, making me a piece of crystal."

The seafront is a huge theater featuring the sunrise. When the curtain of night lifted, the sun comes into the view of the audience with its warm splendor and power. Unfortunately the brilliant performance soon gets so passionate that the audience cannot look at it with naked eyes.

The seafront is the end of many lanes and roads that surprise pedestrians with sudden glimpses of the sea at some seemingly unlikely places.

The beaches are cushions placed between the sea and the city, allowing them to meet politely. The clear water is so refreshing, the azure sky so high, that you feel you are experiencing the tranquility you once felt when you were in the warm womb.

Qingdao has nearly 10 beaches where people come to pay their tribute to the sea by immersing themselves in it every summer.

The sea has so many things to tell you as long as you know how to read it. Its capes and bays, shoals and rocks are inviting to many tourists.

Though overshadowed by the skyscrapers nearby, the solid rocks remain. They are the footnote of the evolution of the city, offering clues of the past.

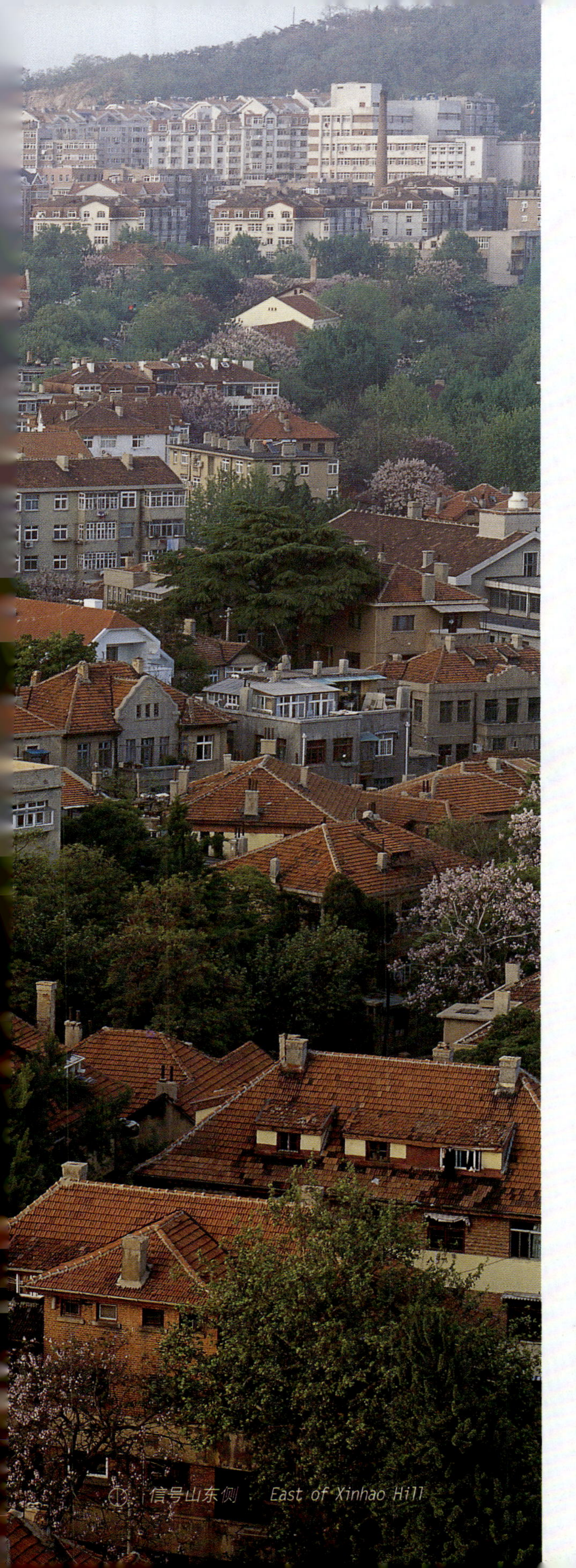

信号山东侧 East of Xinhao Hill

岸衔着街道。临海的街，走着走着，一抬头或一转弯，都可能与海撞个满怀。东山魁夷关于风景的文章《与弗里德希邂逅》可以提醒任何一个行走者，偶遇之美在于自然，自然之美在于青岛的海岸。

沙滩的存在，让岸进入大海的角度分外温柔。青岛大陆架舒缓，湛蓝的海水几乎一眼望穿。在如此质地的水中游泳，会觉得自己很干净、很性感、很年轻、很柔韧、很有力量、很大神通。尤其是余热就要被微风吹散的傍晚，天边的太阳正以玫瑰色谢幕，中空一片冰蓝，悠闲的光亮如此漫长。海水与肌肤的亲爱，让人重温了曾拥有过的母腹生活。

青岛有近十个海水浴场，周边数条通往浴场的路上，梧桐侧立。每个夏天，在梧桐树的茂盛光影里穿行的，是人们对于游泳这一赋予肢体最大解放运动的崇拜！

海百读而不厌。太平角海域又因为小岬角和小湾的变化愈显丰富。角与湾，游戏一样互动着，互动之后甩出几个不大的滩；礁群看似凌乱，却也是经过自然这把鬼斧精雕过的，风浪的身形都可在上面寻到，据说还有别处难得一见的蓝色礁岩。鱼特别喜欢在此游弋，惹得垂钓者成群结队。上世纪二三十年代，现代女作家、文学研究家苏雪林曾写下散文集《岛居漫兴》，其中在《太平角之午》中有如下描写："沿角一带海岸崖石，峥嵘竞秀，又是汇泉浴场所无。有一处景色更为特别。一座大崖，崛起于平地，高约十数丈，远望似一朵吐自海面的紫云，近视则石色黝然，棱棱如积铁，还带着斑驳陆离黄色的铁锈，我怀疑它是属于矿物质，并非真的石头。"

如今，雄性的礁石就在城市的脚下，发散着被压抑的荷尔蒙。当城市沿着海岸长大，发育成熟，婆娑可人，尘封的往事就成了一种注解。这样的注解除了可以让后人索骥某些来龙，让过来人获取某些去脉，更可以让城市拥有某些纪念。

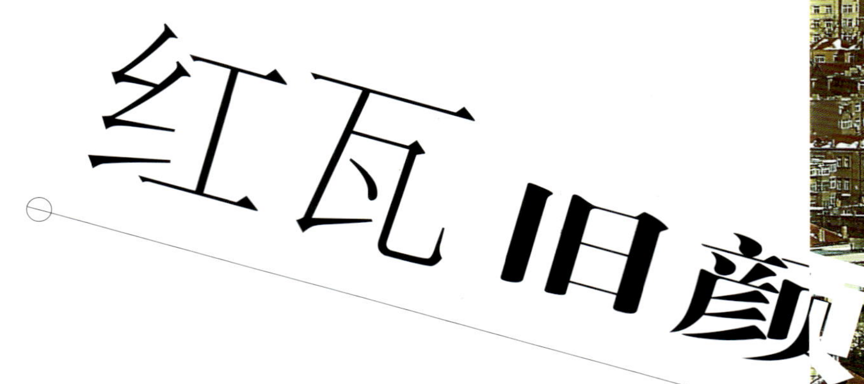

建筑会说话，古旧的红瓦是话锋里的情意，妩媚而笃定。

一百多年前，沂水路被殖民主义的政治家、外交官们瓜分，岛城最早的红瓦由此诞生，与青岛特有的花岗岩"崂山红"、"莱阳绿"、"芝麻白"中的上品一起构成了别墅主体，传递着厚重的艺术美感，演绎出岛城最早的别墅区。短短300米的身段，竟也汇聚了德、英、美、法、日等不同风格的建筑。

德占时的青岛在城市设计上提倡中世纪时欧洲城市的自由活泼、景色如画的规划手法，依照流行于欧洲的"带形城市"和"花园式住宅"的规划思想，德意志民族式古典复兴、浪漫主义和折衷主义在青岛的土地上构成了欧洲近代城市风貌。沂水路上的别墅一般低层有外廊，别墅的主入口呈不规则自由开敞；檐口、屋面、窗帽、门桶的线脚注重装饰性。四个立面考虑到了呼应、对话关系，以券柱廊作为连续的构图母题，富有韵律。

With so many anecdotes to tell, the red tiles on the houses are like the appealing tones of an eager and confident storyteller.

About 100 years ago, politicians and diplomats chose to settle down on Yishui Road. The 300-meter-long road was lined with villas in exotic styles. But most chose to use red tiles, which has shaped the tradition and the feature of Qingdao's architecture.

The early version of the city planning was heavily influenced by the Germans. Ring belts, garden houses, parlors, foyers, decorative patterns on the windows and doors are all of European taste.

① 黄昏中的鱼山路
Yushan Road at sunset

信号山下的民居
Residences around Xinhao Hill

上世纪20年代，城市建筑沿起伏的海岸线东进，渐次触摸到陌生僻远的太平角。太平角的命运恰如其名，它幸运地躲过了军事布防的宿命，而按全新的城市规划，一开始便作为“特别规划区”出现在世人的视线里，吸引城市花园别墅区东移太平角，不久便孕化出一张簇新的城市名片——八大关。

乌瞰天主教堂(圣弥爱尔大教堂)
A bird's-eye view of the Catholic Church

In the1920s, the city started to extend westward along the coast toward Taipingjiao (literally meaning a corner of peace). Later by good luck it was excluded from military construction planning. The current city planning defines it as a special area, and a most appealing business card of Qingdao emerges.

In the 1930s, some foreign adventurers and seafarers came to explore the mysterious Orient just to find Badaguan a perfect place to be their home. They settled down, carving the symbol of a helm above the door to remind them of the start of a new life right here, next to this stretch of water. The houses they built were of a variety of styles: German, Spanish, British, French and Japanese, making it resemble the venue of an international exhibition. From 1929 to 1937, the house styles in Qingdao became various, each standing for a certain moment in the history.

老市政府夜色(原德占时期的总督府)
The old city hall at night (the former German Governor's office)

① 银妆素裹
Snow crested

② 迎宾馆
The Guest House

进入上世纪30年代，西方一些富有的冒险家和航海家漂洋过海，到神秘东方寻找乐土。八大关的碧海黄沙让这样的漂泊嘎然而止，于是，他们把船舵变成象形图案装饰在建筑上，以纪念冒险的终结，同时也开始了临海听潮的逍遥。八大关别墅群因此而丰满，建筑式样也不再是某种单

In light of Qingdao's terrain and climate, the villas all have underground basement which can both reduce moisture and make the floor level. Above the cellars are granite wall base, the walls and cornice. In some cases, the entrances are right in the middle with helms and round paned windows on the top and a pillar on each side.

The boarding walls around the villas in Qingdao are short and hollow, serving to define the space rather than defending or hiding the courtyard. Some of them are so decorative that you are reminded of laces of a skirt. The roof is deliberately treated to be both heatproof and elegant.

The villas are facing the south or the sea to get optimum sunshine in winter and cool sea breeze in summer. The French windows certainly contribute to the same purpose. Vines predominate the court-yard by crawling up and down along any support they can get.

一风格的延续，西班牙式、英国式、德国式、法国式、日本式等风格的相互渗透和拼凑，形成“万国建筑博览会”。也就是说，1929年至1937年间，青岛的庭院式住宅除仿德式外，更出现了和洋折衷小住宅以及清新简洁的现代风格的国际式住宅，每个阶段的建筑都对不同的历史瞬间做着真实的表述。

青岛的别墅群完全依地势而建，为了隔潮，也为了适应地势的高低而做了局部的地下室，墙基采用花岗

The old houses in the old downtown have witnessed and recorded many life stories, either comic or tragic, the old houses seem to be quite sophisticated.

① 平原路 *Pingyuan Road*

天主教堂一侧
Outside of the Catholic Church

基督教堂内景
Inside of the Christian Church

福山路别墅
A villa on Fushan Road

绿树掩映老建筑
An old architecture shadowed by trees

岩，与屋顶檐口、屋身构成完整的三段式立面。有的别墅中轴线与主入口重叠，入口上方凹嵌着船舵与玻璃契合的装饰物——那是一扇透露着美妙的圆形大窗。一层的左右两侧通常为对称式廊柱，既有承重作用，又与主体壁柱相呼应。

围墙是强化别墅风格的点睛之笔。青岛的别墅围墙只属于空间的一种界定，并无明显的防御功能，一般都较矮，而且透空，建筑的全貌没有遮挡。

① 禹城路上的望火楼　The fire-watch tower on Yucheng Road

⑤ 栖霞路别墅
A villa on Qixia Road

① 圣保罗教堂
St. Paul Church

① 太平角一路别墅
A villa on Taipingjiao Yilu Road

② 德占时期胶澳观象台旧址
The site of the Observatory built during German occupation

① 德占时期伯恩尼克住宅
Bernick's residence during the German Occupation

② 八大关一角
A corner of Badaguan

有的围墙以燕巢造型的墙垛串联，其装饰性会让人联想到裙子的花边。为避免日晒，别墅主体屋顶为四坡顶，上下层次分明，屋脊线压砖，层间及檐部多以水平重叠线脚或不同材料进行分隔，使整体立面显得工整紧凑。

别墅的主入口通常朝向大海和温暖的南方，充足的阳光与清朗的海风巡回着，落地窗无法阻隔它们对室内的侵略。园内的植被主题是藤类，或伏地而游，或攀缘而上，通过一个个真实的依靠，顺从地舒展着自我的美丽，柔曼的曲线与别墅的主体走势相互映衬，很是妥当。

老城区和老房子都是生命凝练生命的场所。如今，红瓦旧颜，旧掉的是千回百转的情绪。每一幢别墅都几易房主，在吞噬了几代人的华年之后，散发出灵气和妖气，以兀自的方式，实实在在地记录着不该忘记的过去。

如今，红瓦本身，因为周围物境的变迁，而忧郁，而凄美。

公主楼
Princess's Villa

迎宾馆彩石墙
The colorful stone wall around the Guest House

海大校园
The campus of the Ocean University of China

⦶ 德式建筑一角
Part of a German-style roof

⦸ 德占时期伯恩尼克住宅
Bernick's residence during the German Occupation

发达大
中山路
ZHONGSHAN RD.

历经沧桑的广西路
Guangxi Road

老街往事

一些波浪般起伏的老街主宰着西城的走势。于是，西城曼妙起来，顺带缓解着钢筋水泥的呆板。

老街临海，在潮汐的咏叹里一天天旧掉。老街有主次，宽绰一些的通常与海岸平行，条条街接着，一直通往东城。而那些蛇行的分支已经变成了凋敝的小巷，慌乱的石板伴随丝绒样的苔藓依稀如昨，临街的窗户低低地挂在胡同一边，伸手可及，让人不得不替窗户里的秘密和安全担心。总有老妪拄着拐杖，松懈地站在尽头，盲目地张望着正午白花花的天空，当太阳变成了舞台上的顶光，这个演员却是糙布里没有瓤的玩偶。据说，这样的房子，都是从前的香艳之地，切肤而邻的房间，美丽与腐烂曾经紧挨着。

主街当然不同，即使旧了，也底气十足。其中，莱阳路是青岛最早的路之一。因为秉承了德国人将其规划为夏季度假别墅区的功能，莱阳路

The zigzagging roads on the hilly terrain add romance and variation to the city's concrete construction.

The undulating streets adjacent to the sea are aging in the sea mist. The busy ones are parallel with the coast leading to the new district on the east. The narrow branches of the main streets have seen better days. They are deserted and moss-grown, with puppet-like old ladies leaning on crutches in broad daylight.

The busy main streets are old too, but still impressive. Laiyang Road is among the earliest streets constructed. It is in the area originally designed to be a summer resort, so buildings along the road are no more than 3 storeys high, with gardens, courtyard, garages and balconies. On the south of the road is Luxun Park, one of the best places to go for a walk.

Taiping Road, another busy old street, is the immediate neighbor of the sea. Along the road you will get to the sword-like Pier, the most appealing place for the tourists, then a temple dating back to the Ming Dynasty. Many local people still come to the temple to burn incense, praying for safe journeys of the sailors.

栈盈宾馆

兰山路路口
A street corner on Lanshan Road

上的建筑全部依照庭院式坐落，有楼、有院、有山坡、有车库、有露天的观海阳台。花砖铺地形成多变的图案，临街建筑不会高过三层，界面柔和，有凸凹，可以容下玲珑石凳的组合；镂空或雕花的黑铁门，燕窝一样的阁楼，花石墙上缠绕着藤萝。所以，莱阳路是海的后花园。过了向南的马路，就进入了鲁迅公园，公园与海密不可分，风起的日子，甬道常常被海浪打湿。

在青岛最早的路中，太平路也是红到今天的主角。除了护栏，太平路与海之间没有间隔，如果满月，站在太平路上，几乎伸手就能捞起海面上碎银般的月光。有了太平路才有了百年栈桥，栈桥是一把从太平路插入大海的剑。走在桥上，层层海浪涌来，拍打堤坝，击起碎玉万千。早在明代，太平路上就建有一座天后宫，专门用来保佑出海的人平安归来，保佑风平浪静鱼满仓，直到现在，仍然香火不断。

老街漫步，潮音盈耳如同天籁。这时候，你会爱上行走。你甚至想，如果能一直沿着海走，你愿意走到死。你甚至自诩，一个城市可以没有职业思想家，但喜欢在街上闲逛的人，一定离思想不太远。

事实上，老街除了可以激发哲学姿态，更是通向欢乐天堂的路径。

沿着海，向东。当南海路与海构成一个温柔的锐角，第一海水浴场已然变成了南海路的延伸，同时，沙滩的娱乐性也使南海路沉淀了太多的欢声笑语，演绎出无数与自然通灵的方式，更

雅戈尔
Eastern
雅戈尔
中华商
烤肉店

∅ 曲阜路路口
A street corner on Qvfu Road

The sound of waves you hear on these streets justifies a daily walk along the coast. It is not surprising if insights storm your brain and you are inclined to ponder upon some philosophical issues.

Nanhai Road is the eastern extension of No.1 Bathing Beach, which is a popular place for the locals to enjoy themselves in summer. Taipingjiao Erlu Road features phoenix trees and red tiles. Castles, capes and cliffs set scene for dramatic imaginations.

鱼山路新貌
Renovated Yushan Road

成为制造幸福事件的绝对场所。

沿着海，向东再向东。太平角二路也是一条与沙滩缱绻相连的路。光阴留痕，连那梧桐懒散的绿荫也已年深日久，殖民时期的老房子如衰老的贵妇，红色蒙莎式瓦筒敛住了最后的冶艳。整个太平角，陆域由湛山一路至五路、太平角一路至五路组成，若干风格独特的建筑攀伏其上。海边、峭崖、岬角、古堡——当这些词汇融于一体的时候，戏剧性的身段便迎面走来。

老街是可以感知脚步节奏的回音壁，或舒缓、或骤急、或与心跳合拍、或与潮汐共生。老街依原始地貌或逶迤、或跌宕、或幽闭，最大程度地上演着人与往事、老街与城、城与生活的情景剧——这样的剧情值得期望。

鱼山支路
A branch of Yushan Road

石路回望

石路有凹凸，且泛着幽远的青光。岁月默然地歇伏其上，缝隙里有鸟儿衔来的种子，发了绿芽，小诗一般。

鱼肠子一样的石路躺在小胡同里，一咏三叹着。因为鲜有车辆穿梭，所以，发动机粗糙的喘息声被删除了。但这并不代表石路是封闭的或拒绝沟通的，只不过它沟通的方式更富有人文色彩——常常是这样，一条倾斜的石路可以衔接三条大路，直到通往更远的远方。

石路上很少商业门脸，一切都很瓷实。日常的作息沉淀下来，节奏异常舒缓，甚至有些停滞。说白了，石路都是一些没有惊艳、没有颤栗、没有冲动的路，只有陈年老树在无可自抑地疯长。光线透过枝杈跌落在石路上，光与影的游戏没有休止。

岛城的石路少不了海雾的浸润。尤其是那些多雾的晚春时节，夜色方显，海雾便须臾而上，瞬间濡湿了石路。而在初夏的清晨，5点钟的时候太阳还未醒，石路上却已隐约着茴香的甜味，谁走在上面，呼吸都要贪婪起来。

岛城石路的美丽在于它的不规则，布局因势摆设，没有图纸规划，一切随遇而安。石路两旁有老宅，几根竹竿搭在石路上空，五颜六色的衣服便飘扬起来。宅子里的住户常常在石路上会客，仿佛石路就是他们家的会客厅。夏夜，石路又成了纳凉的天地，一巷子里的人围成一个大圈，海阔天空地闲

THE STONE-FACED Roads

Though undulated, the stone-faced roads wriggles their way to the main roads. Shops are seldom found along the roads, which means the roads offer the pedestrians less, or even no surprise nor thrill. Sunshine filters through the lonely branches and twigs of trees on a winter day.

The stone roads are found moist and a little slippery with sea mist at dawn or in the evening in late spring. Together with the scent of the trees on both sides, the stone roads have enchanted many visitors.

The charm of the stone roads is its irregularity, its creative and discretionary adaptation to the hilly

沂水路旁的庭院
A courtyard next to Yishui Road

鱼山支路
A branch of Yushan Road

福山路和栖霞路间的石阶
Stone Steps connecting
Fushan Road and Qixia Road

侃，侃得不着边际，反正没人追究。

石路很窄，住户的院子更小。这家屋檐连着那家屋檐，层层叠叠，挤挤挨挨。这家一声咳嗽，那家如在耳畔。小院四周一圈篱笆，蔷薇、牵牛花、紫藤、爬山虎拼命地攀缘而上，为石路带来了花期，花期可遇不可求，一阵风，开了；又一阵风，便谢了。

石路延伸着城市的性格，凹凸的路面是城市历史的刻度。胶东路、黄岛路、肥城路、波罗油子……城市在长大，更多的石路不得不真实地消失了。那些曾经顽固的生活方式和地域性特征，也在城市概念中溶解，只留下某个沧桑的名字，以纪念洗刷不掉的记忆。

⦶ 老路沧桑
An old road

terrain. The picture would not be complete if I do not mention the colorful clothes hung on the bamboo rods put across the roads by the residents, and the rose bushes, morning glories and ivy along the roads. The residents, their neighbors and friends, used to form circles on the roads, chatting, laughing under the starry skies at summer nights. Narrow roads, cozy courtyard made the neighborhood warmer and closer.

The roads are often the mirror of the nature and history of the city. You can not talk about Qingdao without mentioning such names as Jiaodong Road, Huangdao Road and Feicheng Road. Boluoyouzi (a stone–faced road), so typical of Qingdao, are gone with the transformation of the city. The names, however, shall remain to remind people of the past.

青岛市人民政府新闻办公室 / 主编

书　　名　欧韵青岛
摄　　影　王超鲁　薛晨钟　秦　岭
撰　　文　王占筠
翻　　译　李　力　刘　静
出版发行　青岛出版社
社　　址　青岛市徐州路77号（266071）
本社网址　http://www.qdpub.com
邮购电话　13335059110　（0532）80998664
传　　真　（0532）85814750
责任编辑　申　尧
装帧设计　习　习
制版印刷　青岛海蓝印刷有限责任公司
版　　次　2005年10月第3版
　　　　　2007年4　月第4次印刷
开　　本　12开（787×1092mm）
印　　张　6
书　　号　ISBN978-7-5436-0229-8
定　　价　58.00元